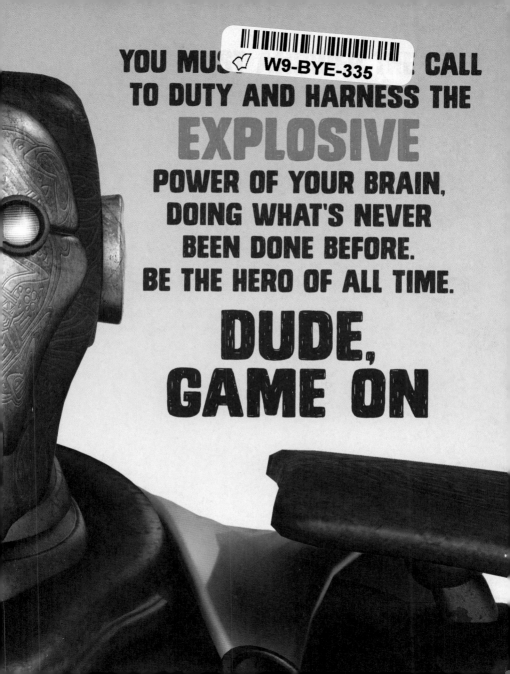

FOLLOW ME
TO THE POINT
OF NO RETURN.

DUDE DIARY
UNLOCK THE POWER!

CREATED BY

MICKEY
AND
CHERYL
GILL

AS WE RAN FROM THE
ZOMBIE APOCALYPSE

FINE print
PUBLISHING

Fine Print Publishing Company
P.O. Box 916401
Longwood, Florida 32791-6401

Created in the U.S.A. & Printed in China
This book is printed on acid-free paper.

ISBN 9781-89295172-4

2 3 5 7 9 10 8 6 4 1

thedudebook.com

PROPERTY OF:

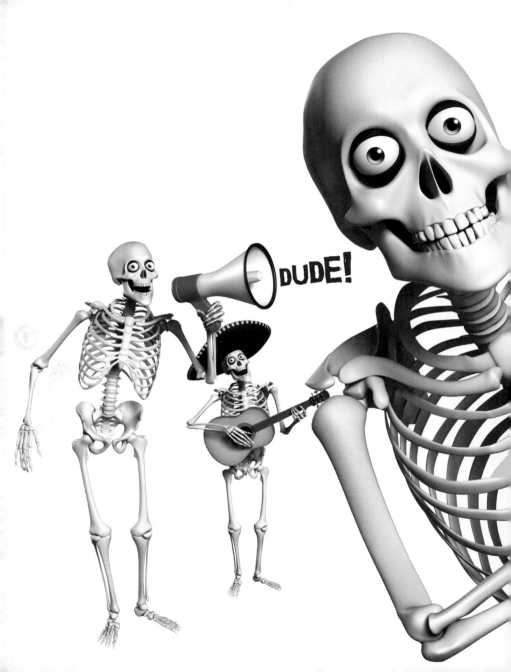

BE AFRAID. BE VERY AFRAID.

COMMUNICATE WITH AN ALIEN,
HANG WITH A CAVE MAN,
GO UNDERCOVER AS A WILD ANIMAL,
CHART THE FILTHIEST STUFF IN YOUR
LIFE, AND FILL JARS WITH THE
NASTIEST THINGS EVER.

KEEP YOUR PLANS HIDDEN AWAY
IN YOUR DUDE
DIARY.
GUARD THEM
WITH YOUR
LIFE.

WOULD YOU RATHER LIVE IN A WORLD FULL OF ZOMBIES OR DINOSAURS

OR BOTH?

WHY? AND HOW WOULD YOU PROTECT YOURSELF?

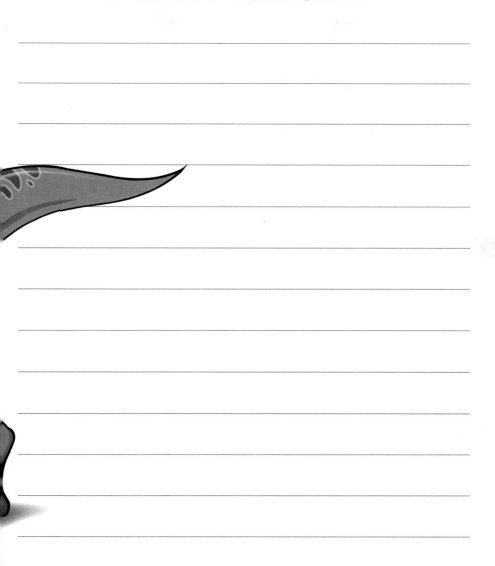

WHAT ARE YOU TOTALLY TERRIFIED TO DO?

WHAT WOULD BE REALL
SCHOOL'S INTERCOM
OR TV?

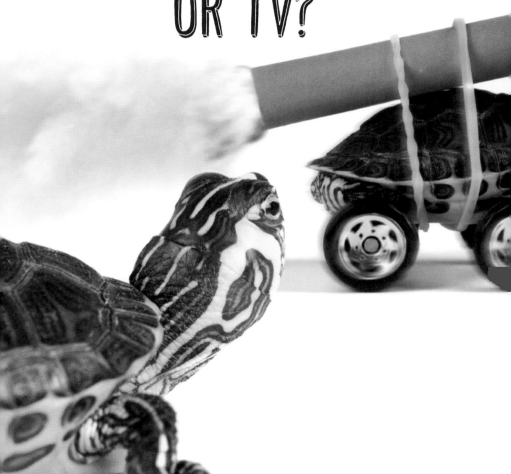

UNNY TO DO OVER THE

COMMANDER COBBLER

IS THE LEADER OF

CORE –

A RACE OF HUMANOID-LIKE, UNDERGROUND APPLES THAT HAVE RISEN UP TO THE EARTH'S SURFACE. THEY HAVE EVIL PLANS FOR WORLD DOMINATION AND OUTNUMBER US FIVE TO ONE. HOW SHOULD WE TAKE DOWN THESE FRUITY FOES?

_____

_____

_____

_____

_____

_____

_____

WHAT DID YOU SEND DOWN THE SINK TODAY?

Dead skin cells.

Broccoli from my teeth.

WRITE EVERYTHING ƧQЯAWꞰƆAꓭ.

FINISH DRAWING THE *BEAST*

GIVE IT A NAME

{ }

WHAT MAKES IT ANGRY?

{ }

WHAT'S ITS FAVORITE KIND OF SMOOTHIE?

{ }

Give everyone super powers and new superhero names.

Name

Super Power

Superhero Name

A METEORITE
EXPLODES
IN THE ATMOSPHERE,
RAINING ALIEN ENERGY
OVER YOUR
NEIGHBORHOOD!
You, your family, & your best friend now have
SUPER POWERS!

IT'S A WRAP!

THINK OF YOUR FAVORITE FOODS. COMBINE 5 OF THEM INTO AN INSANELY COOL WRAP!

_____

food name

ON TOP OF

_____

food name

ON TOP OF

_____

food name

ON TOP OF

_____

food name

ON TOP OF

_____

food name

ALL MUSHED TOGETHER IN A BIG FAT WRAP.
NOW GIVE IT A CRAZY NAME

WOULD YOU RATHER...

OWN A
- ○ ROBOTIC DOG
- ○ YETI HOLOGRAM?

HAVE PURPLE
- ○ HAIR ○ HANDS?

COMPETE IN A
- ○ HOT DOG
- ○ PIE EATING CONTEST?

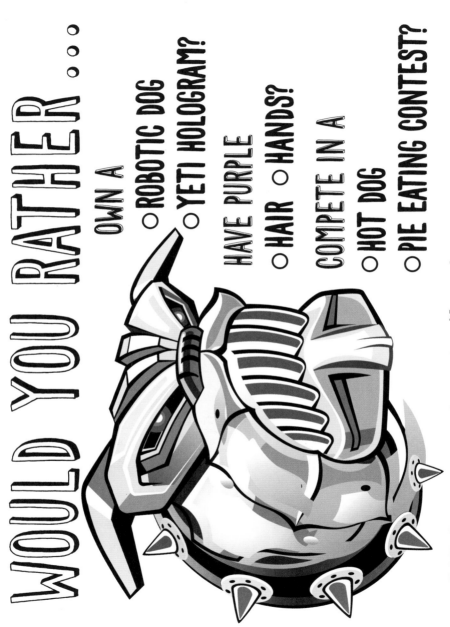

WRESTLE A GIANT ○ MAN-EATING CACTUS ○ RUNNING NOSE?

○ DANCE IN A BIG VAT OF WET NOODLES

○ SWIM IN A POOL OF CHOCOLATE SYRUP?

Go ahead ... I dare you.

EAT

○ FISH EGGS

○ OCTOPUS TENTACLES?

HAVE

○ SPIDER LEGS

○ A RAT TAIL?

Gross! My legs on a human torso?!

○ CLIMB THE TALLEST MOUNTAIN

○ SCALE THE TALLEST SKYSCRAPER?

○ SINGING FARTS ○ SONIC BOOM BELCHES?

○ KNOW A TON OF BIG WORDS

○ BE ABLE TO SOLVE COMPLICATED MATH PROBLEMS?

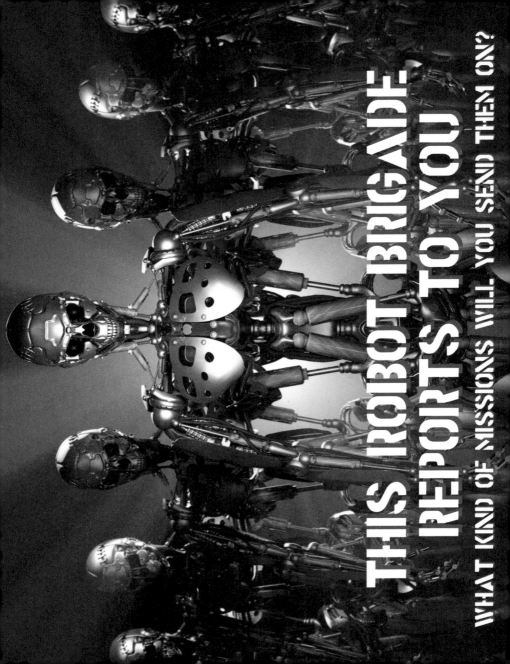

THIS ROBOT BRIGADE
REPORTS TO YOU

WHAT KIND OF MISSIONS WILL YOU SEND THEM ON?

1.

2.

3.

4.

5.

WhAt COOL thINGS COULD YOU DO tOGEthER?

_____

_____

WhERE ShOULD YOU tAKE hIM?

_____

_____

WhAt WILL YOU tEACh hIM tO DO?

_____

_____

WhICh FOODS ShOULD YOU INtRODUCE hIM tO?

_____

_____

FILL THESE JARS WITH COOL, DISGUSTING, DELICIOUS, OR OUTRAGEOUS STUFF YOU'D LIKE TO COLLECT.

WHAT WOULD YOU TEACH?

HOW WOULD YOU GET KIDS TO LIKE YOU?

WHAT WOULD YOU DO IN THE TEACHER'S LOUNGE?

1. CHOOSE A LOCKER TO OPEN.

2. TURN THE BOOK UPSIDE DOWN TO DISCOVER WHAT'S GUARDING THE PRIZE.

3. DESCRIBE YOUR PLAN OF ATTACK TO SCORE THE AWESOME LOOT.

BLUE- ELECTRIFIED PLATYPUS   GREEN- FEROCIOUS, ANKLE-BITING TROLL   YELLOW- ZOMBIE   RED- DRAGON

IF YOU COULD CHOOSE WHO LIVED IN YOUR NEIGHBORHOOD WHO (OR WHAT) WOULD YOU PICK?

Oh, we definitely need a ninja master next door.

WHAT WOULD YOU DO WITH YOUR POWER?

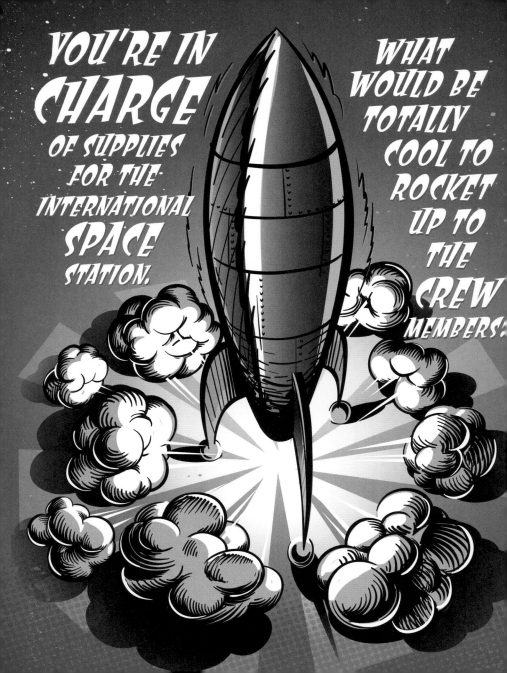

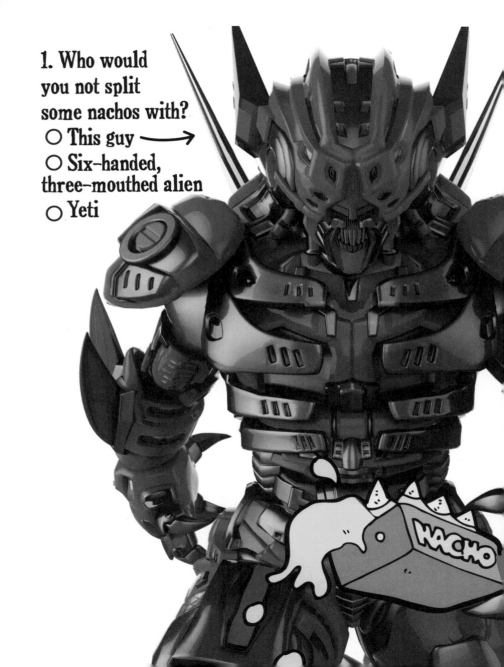

1. Who would you not split some nachos with?
○ This guy ⟶
○ Six-handed, three-mouthed alien
○ Yeti

2. Contest you're pretty sure you'd win? _____

_____

3. What would you pay money to see?
      ○ Tarantula circus ○ Octopus paintball game

4. Would you rather be able to
  ○ bend your legs over your shoulders ○ belch like a walrus?

5. Fake ○ roach ○ barf ○ vampire teeth ○ mustache?

6. What would be awesome right now?
    ○ Fried chicken leg ○ Double-fudge anything

7. Disguise that would be awesome to wear? _____

_____

8. Which would be funnier?
    ○ Talking with our ears ○ Eating with our nose

9. What makes you itch just thinking about it?
    ○ Fleas ○ Wool uniform ○ Athlete's foot

10. Would you rather be able to
    ○ breathe fire
    ○ swallow a sword
    ○ perform unbelievable card tricks?

MAKE AN INSANELY AWESOME MONSTER TRUCK

TRICK IT OUT WITH YOUR OWN DESIGNS AND INCLUDE A COOL NAME.

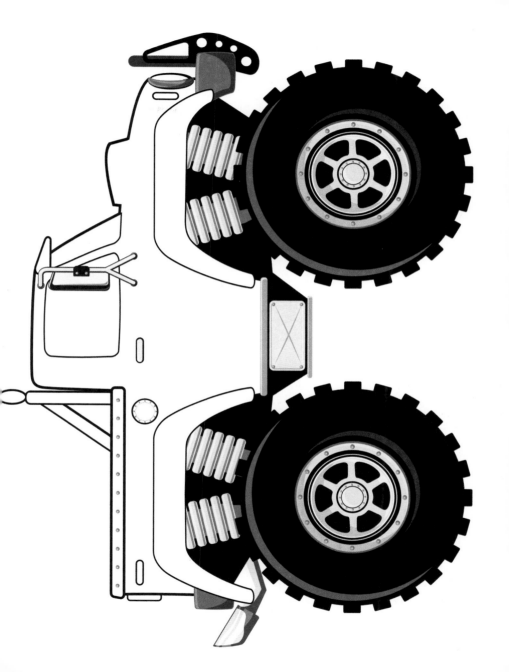

WHICH FOODS WOULD make THE BEST KNOCK-DOWN, DRAG OUT Food fight?

A secret tunnel under your room leads to different locations around the world.

which **5** places would you like to connect with

1.

2.

3.

4.

5.

WHAT ARE THE DIRTIEST THINGS IN YOUR LIFE? RANK THEM FROM 1–10.

1 is the worst.

[ ]RTEST
THING EVER IS

1

2

3

4

5

6

7

8

9

10

CAPE JELLYFISH BOY!

IT'S AMERICA'S NEW SEMI-AQUATIC HERO! HE TAKES THE STING OUT OF CRIME.

HOW SHOULD HE TAKE DOWN CRIMINALS?

WHERE SHOULD HE LIVE?

HOW SHOULD HE RELAX WHEN HE'S NOT FIGHTING CRIME?

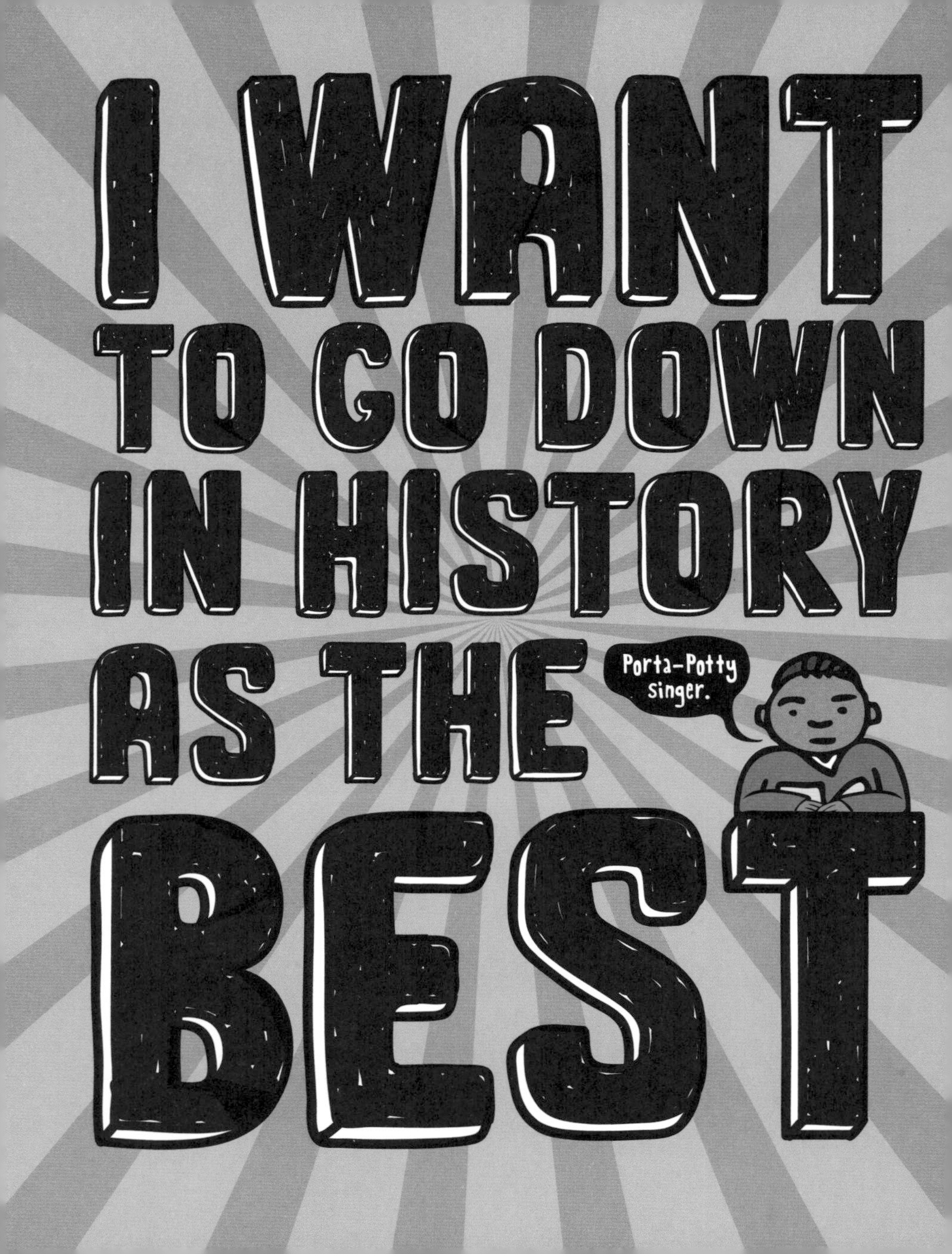
I WANT TO GO DOWN IN HISTORY AS THE BEST
Porta-Potty singer.

A-LARIOUS CRAZY PARADE

Our coaches dressed in tutus.

Draw or describe your creation

EVER AGAIN?

1. Would you rather be a
- **ninja warrior**
- **rocket scientist**
- **celebrity sub sandwich chef?**

2. Dumbest dare you've ever taken?

_____

3. What would be sweet to declare yourself the king of?

_____

4. Which shoe do you put on first? ○ Right   ○ Left

5. Would you rather have
  ○ a bowling alley ○ water flume ○ zipline in your bedroom?

6. What would be an awesome last name for you?
  ○ Thunder ○ Legend ○ Rock ○ Other_____

7. Favorite room in your home you like to chill in?

_____

8. Would you rather have ○ night ○ X-ray vision?

9. If you were a soup-erhero which soup would give you power?

_____

10. What do you think victory tastes like?
  ○ Steak ○ PB & chocolate ○ Deep dish pizza

BUILD A strange MONUMENT

FOR TOURISTS TO VISIT

WHAT WILL YOU BUILD?

WHAT WEIRD STUFF WILL YOU MAKE IT OUT OF?

DRAW IT HERE

A giant kangaroo statue made from dust bunnies.

A snowman made of dandruff flakes.

OPEN ALL DAY

monument name

GIVE YOUR BRAIN A BREAK.

A mirage is an optical illusion that happens in super hot places like the desert.

It can look like water.

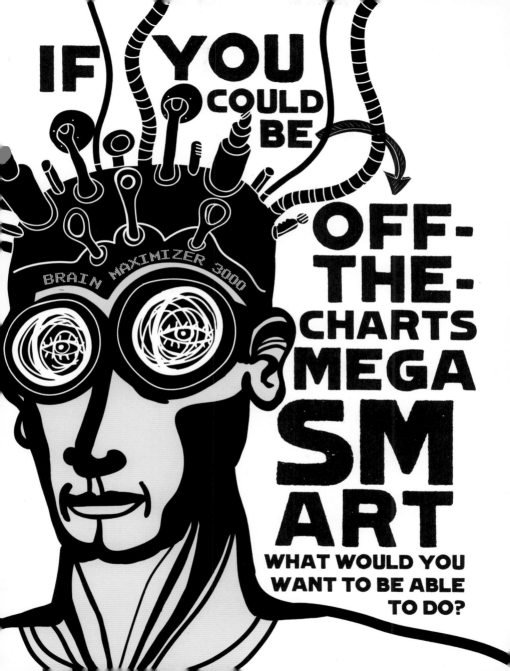

IF YOU COULD BE OFF-THE-CHARTS MEGA SMART WHAT WOULD YOU WANT TO BE ABLE TO DO?

BRAIN MAXIMIZER 3000

WHAT ARE YOUR X-CITING IDEAS FOR CLASSES?

Skateboard around kids in the hall while taking a spelling test.

TO YOUR SCHOOL

CREATE YOUR OWN WEIRD WORLD

WHAT IMPOSSIBLE THINGS WOULD BE POSSIBLE?

WHAT DO YOU NEED TO PULL OUT OF THIS MAGIC HAT TODAY?

RULE YOUR SCHOOL

WITH AN AWESOME

PAD CONTROL PANEL

Fill in the buttons with cool, hilarious, and totally ridiculous things you would love to see happen at school.

I'd turn water into chocolate in all the water fountains!

I'd turn the hallways into a giant ball pit with the push of a button.

BE A PROFESSIONAL
DAREDEVIL

YOUR NEXT FEAT IS A DANGEROUS JUMP

PICK YOUR RIDE

SKATEBOARD · DIRT BIKE · MOTOR BOAT · JET SKI

SNOWBOARD · ROLLER BLADES · SNOW MACHINE

HUMONGOUS BANANA PEEL · OTHER _____

CHOOSE SOMETHING TO JUMP OVER

ELECTRIC SLUGS · CROCODILES · GIANT PIRANHA · BOOGERS · COBRAS

FILL THE TANK WITH YOUR CHOICE

RCOVER

Which animal would you disguise yourself as?

_____

_____

What would you do?

_____

_____

_____

_____

_____

_____

WHERE WAS IT FIRST SPOTTED?

HOW DID IT BECOME HALF CHICKEN & HALF WHATEVER THIS IS?

GIVE IT AN **AH-MAZING** NAME

WHAT DOES IT DO DURING THE DAY? AT NIGHT?

1. _____

2. _____

3. _____

4. _____

5. _____

6. _____

7. _____

8. _____

9. _____

10. _____

Man, where do I start?

Well, first you're gonna need an epic key ring.

YOU'VE BEEN GIVEN A KEY THAT OPENS EVERYTHING ON 🌎 !!!

1. What is most likely to take over the world someday?

- O Dolphins
- O Computers
- O Cyborg Chihuahuas

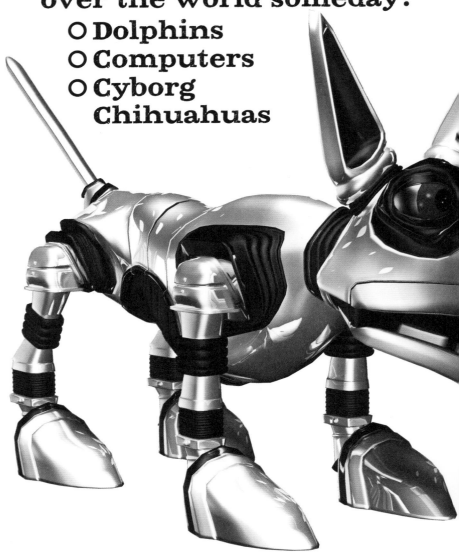

2. Last thing you lost? _____

3. Last thing you found? _____

4. ○ Barbecue ○ Honey mustard ○ Super hot wings?

5. What would be awesome to shoot out of a cannon?

_____

6. Longest word you know?

_____

7. Something you do which could be a funny Olympic sport?

_____

8. Favorite food that melts in your mouth?

_____

YOU WILL
DO AS I
COMMAND/

9. How much money would it take for you to square dance in public?

$

10. Do you insist on getting your way?
  ○ Always ○ Sometimes ○ Never

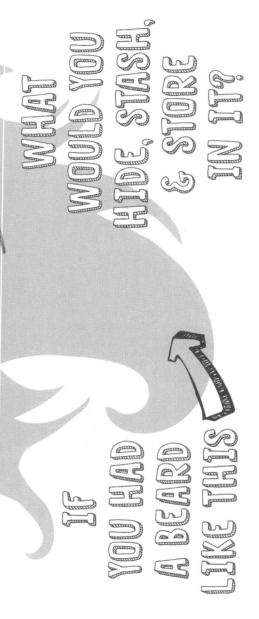

IF YOU HAD A BEARD LIKE THIS

WHAT WOULD YOU HIDE, STASH, & STORE IN IT?

GET YOUR GRUBBY
HAND ON A PEN
OR MARKER. WRITE
UNBELIEVABLE 
THINGS. DRAW LIKE
CRAZY, & DESTROY
IF THINGS GET OUT
OF CONTROL.

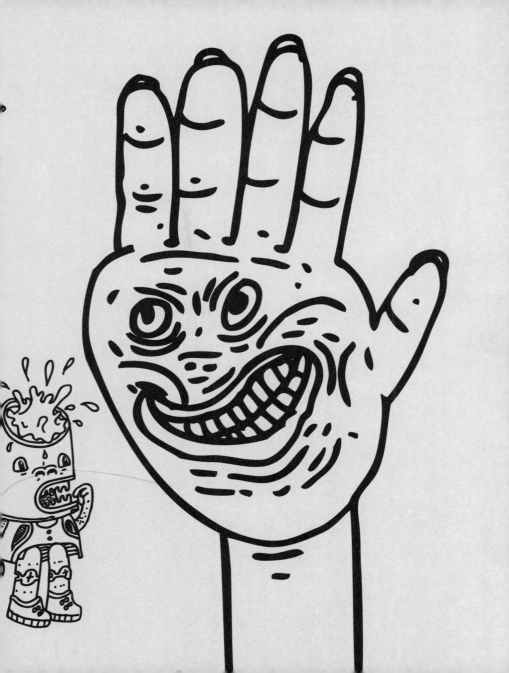

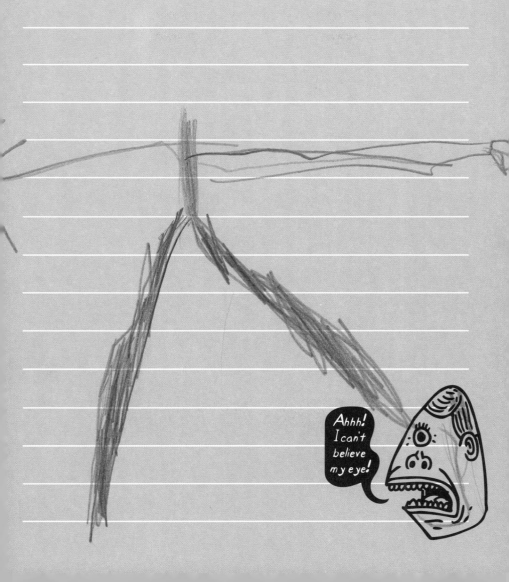

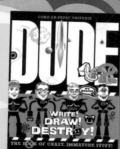